Page 3

Page 17

Page 11

Spare

Pages 20-21

Spare

Page 23

D0412916

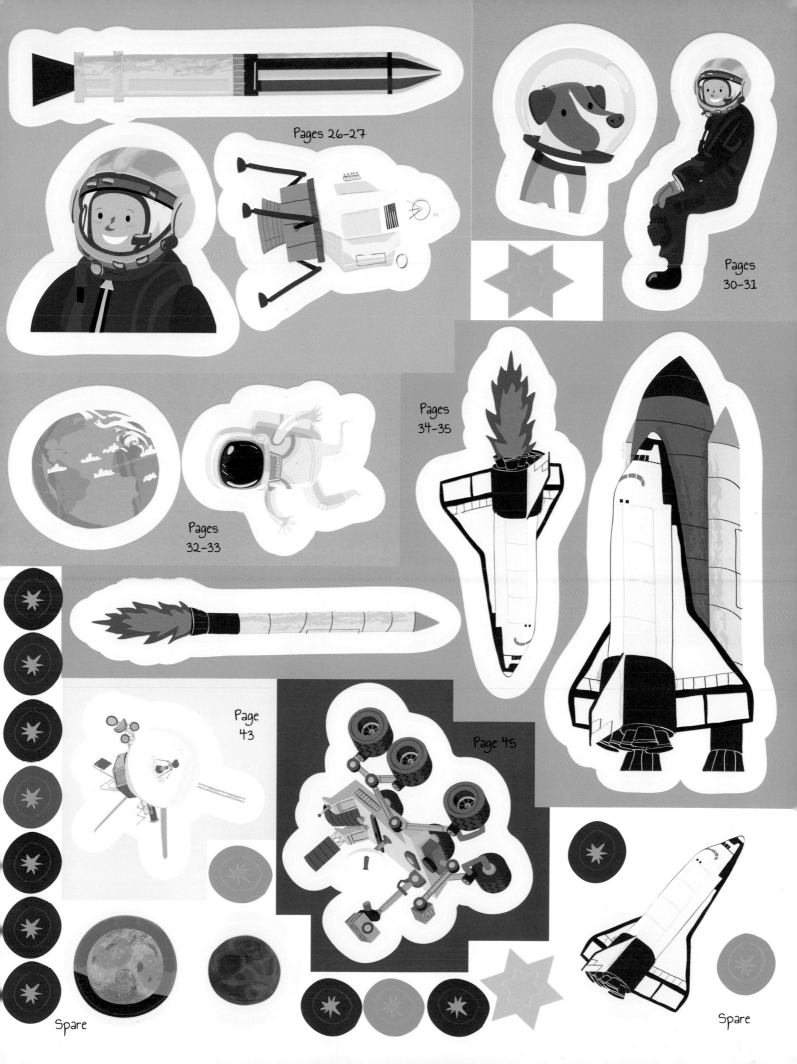

Pages 26-27

Pages 30-31

Pages 34-35

Pages 32-33

Page 43

Page 45

Spare

Spare

Page 7

Pages 8-9

CCCP

Pages 14-15

Pages 24-25

Pages 16-17

Spare

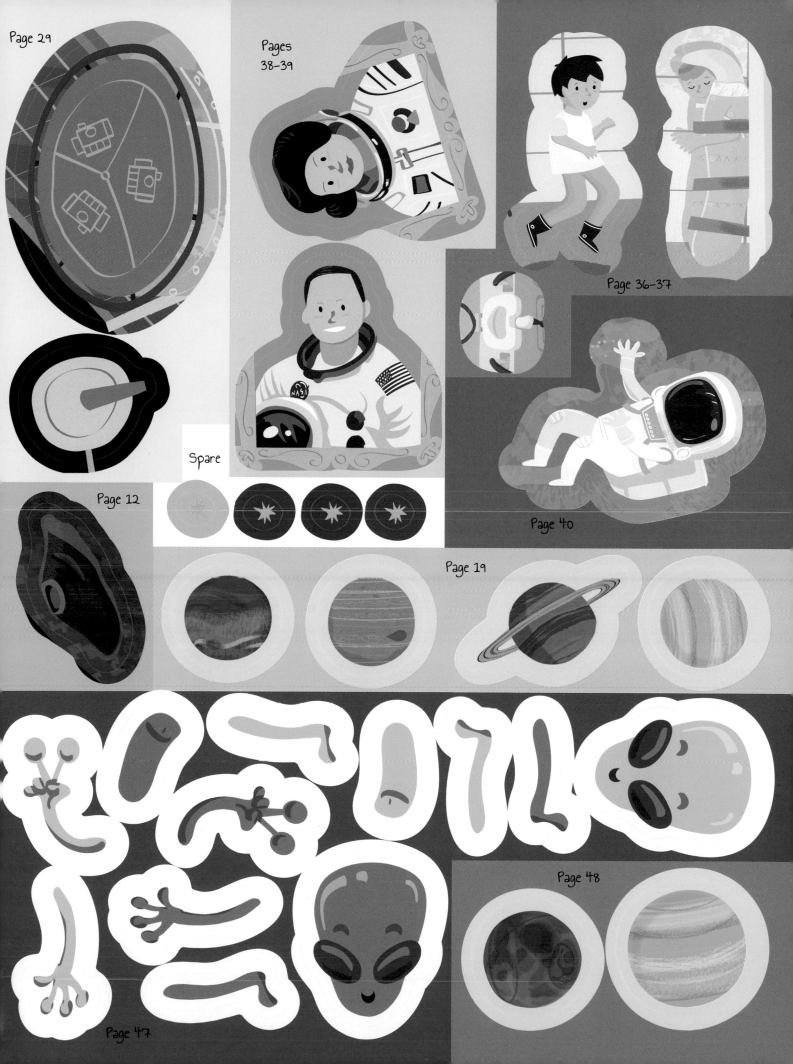

Page 29

Pages 38-39

Page 36-37

Page 12

Spare

Page 40

Page 19

Page 47

Page 48

GLOW-IN-THE-DARK STICKERS

KNOW AND GLOW
SPACE
Sticker Activities

Published by Hinkler Books Pty Ltd
45–55 Fairchild Street
Heatherton Victoria 3202 Australia
www.hinkler.com

hinkler

© Hinkler Books Pty Ltd 2018

Packaged by Collaborate Agency
Prepress: Graphic Print Group

ISBN: 978 1 4889 3500 8

Printed and bound in Malaysia

CONTENTS

THE UNIVERSE

What is the Universe? Well, it's everything that exists! It began about 13.8 billion years ago with a burst of energy known as the Big Bang. As the Universe cooled down, tiny particles of matter formed. Over hundreds of millions of years, some matter formed into stars. About eight billion years later, the Solar System began forming.

Every day new information about space is being discovered by organisations such as NASA (the National Aeronautics and Space Administration). The people working at NASA, and other space-dedicated organisations around the world, dream up new space rovers, plan space missions and feed our fascination for all things in the night sky.

Add the glow-in-the-dark stickers to the Big Bang.

THE SUN AND SOLAR SYSTEM

Our Solar System is made up of the Sun, planets and their moons, asteroids and comets. The Sun is a star at the centre of the Solar System. Although the Solar System is vast, it's only the tiniest part of what's out there in space.

HOW THE SOLAR SYSTEM WAS FORMED

1 Almost 5 million years ago, the solar system was just a cloud of dust and gas. The cloud collapsed, possibly when disturbed by an exploding star.

2 The centre of the cloud became very compressed, creating a disk of gas and dust spinning around it.

3 The pressure in the centre of the cloud caused nuclear reactions that formed our Sun.

4 The leftover material from the reaction gathered together due to gravity.

5 These objects grew to become planets, comets, asteroids and moons.

Mercury

Venus

Earth

Sun

Complete the Solar System by adding the glow-in-the-dark stickers.

Uranus

2 SOLAR SYSTEM FACTS

✹ Mercury, Venus, Earth and Mars formed with rocky surfaces. These are known as the Inner Solar System.

✹ The outer parts of the Solar System were cooler, so the planets that formed there were very different. Jupiter, Saturn, Uranus and Neptune are known as 'gas giants' because they have thick, gassy atmospheres.

Jupiter

Mars

Saturn

3 FUN SUN FACTS

✹ The Sun gives life to Earth because it provides the energy that helps plants grow.

✹ The Sun is the largest object in the Solar System and makes up 99.8 per cent of its total mass.

✹ It takes about 365 days, or one year, for Earth to travel around the Sun once. That's what determines how long a year is on Earth.

Neptune

MERCURY

Mercury is the smallest planet and the closest to the Sun. Be careful where you tread as there are huge craters everywhere. These were formed four billion years ago when Mercury was hit by a large asteroid causing molten rock to burst from its centre. Hundreds of volcanoes were formed which then broke down into craters.

PLANET PROFILE

Distance from Sun:
57.9 million km
(35.9 million miles)

Average Temperature:
167°C (332.6°F)

Moons: 0

Diameter: 4,878 km
(3,031 miles)

It takes Mercury 88 days to orbit the Sun. This is faster than any other planet.

Mercury took 80,000 years to form!

64

63

62

61 •

60 •

59 •

58 •

57 •

56 •

55

54

53 52 51 •

50 •

Join the dots to
find out how the
inspiration for
the planet's name
was represented.

1

2

3

4

5

6

7

8

9

10

11

12

13

14

15

16

17

18

19

20

21

22

23

24

25

26

27

28

29

30

31

32

33

34

35

36

37

38

39

40

41

42

43

44

45

46

47

48

49

Mercury was
named after a
Roman god.

Add the volcano
stickers to the surface
of Mercury.

VENUS

Venus is even hotter than Mercury! It is the brightest of the planets because it has a thick atmosphere around it, which reflects back most of the sunlight that hits it. Venus is almost the same size as Earth.

PLANET PROFILE

Distance from Sun:
108.2 million km
(67.2 million miles)

Average Temperature:
462°C (864°F)

Moons: 0

Diameter: 12,104 km
(7,521 miles)

5 AMAZING VENUS FACTS

Can you guess whether these fascinating statements about Venus are true or false? Write down your answer and then place a reward sticker next to each one that you get right.

a. Venus is the coldest of the eight planets.

b. Venus is the furthest planet from Earth.

Venera 7 was launched to Venus in 1970 to send data from the planet's atmosphere. It was the first spacecraft to send back data after landing on another planet.

CCCP

Find the sticker of the Venera 7 Lander.

EXPLORE MORE

There are many websites with lots of information about space missions. To learn more, ask an adult to help you find them!

c. Venus is approximately the same size as Earth.

d. There are over 1,600 volcanoes on the surface of Venus.

e. The carbon dioxide surrounding Venus is not poisonous.

EARTH AND THE MOON

Why is Earth the only planet in the Solar System where animals and plants survive? It's because there's water and oxygen here. Earth is surrounded by a thick layer of gases called the atmosphere. This gives us the oxygen we need to breathe. The atmosphere also lets in light and heat from the Sun and keeps out its harmful rays too.

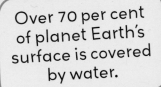

Over 70 per cent of planet Earth's surface is covered by water.

Inner Core

Outer Core

Mantle

Crust

PLANET PROFILE

Distance from Sun:
149.6 million km
(93 million miles)

Average Temperature:
15°C (59°F)

Moons: 1

Diameter: 12,756 km
(7,926 miles)

This diagram shows the phases of the moon seen from Earth's northern hemisphere. In the southern hemisphere, the phases are reversed.

Earth is made up of layers called the crust, mantle, outer core and inner core.

* Just as Earth travels around the Sun, the Moon travels around Earth. Like Earth, all parts of the Moon have days and nights.

* The Moon does not give out light but it reflects light from the Sun.

* As the Moon orbits Earth the amount of the sunlit part we see changes. These changes are known as the 'phases' of the Moon.

Fill in the phases of the Moon with the glow-in-the-dark stickers.

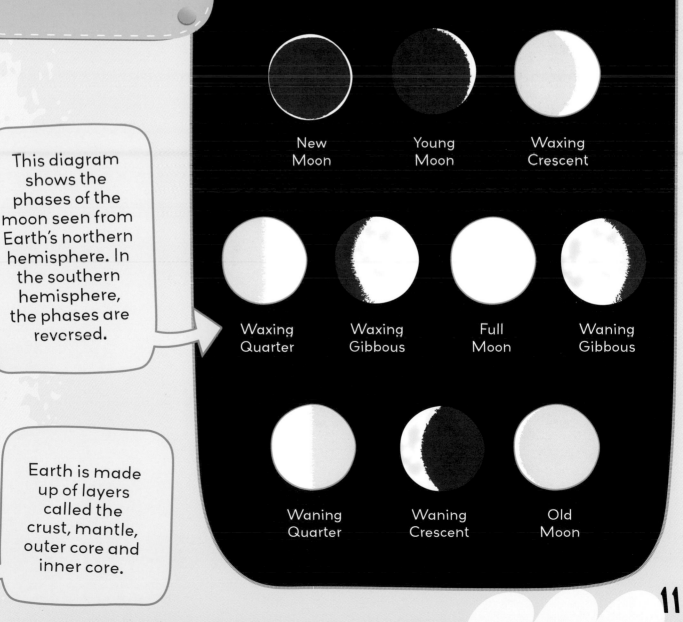

New Moon

Young Moon

Waxing Crescent

Waxing Quarter

Waxing Gibbous

Full Moon

Waning Gibbous

Waning Quarter

Waning Crescent

Old Moon

MARS

Mars is named after the Roman god of War. It has a red, rocky outer layer, which is why it is often called the Red Planet. Mars is extremely cold and is known for its very strong red dust storms.

PLANET PROFILE

Distance from Sun:
227.9 million km
(141.6 million miles)

Average Temperature:
−63°C (−85°F)

Moons: 2

Diameter: 6,779 km
(4,212 miles)

Olympus Mons on Mars is the largest volcano in the Solar System. It is 25 km (15.5 miles) tall, which is almost three times the height of Mount Everest.

Find the sticker of Olympus Mons.

2 FACTS ABOUT MARS

✷ The colour of the red sands on Mars come from their rich rust content.

✷ Mars has a permanent cap of water ice at its North and South poles.

LIFE ON MARS

Make up a life form that you think could live on Mars and draw it here.

JUPITER

Jupiter is the largest planet in the Solar System. It is so big it could fit all of the other seven planets inside it! A huge storm known as the Great Red Spot has been raging in Jupiter's atmosphere for more than 300 years and is twice the size of Earth.

PLANET PROFILE

Distance from Sun:
778.3 million km
(483.6 million miles)

Average Temperature:
−150°C (−240°F)

Moons: Around 70, with more discovered almost every year!

Diameter: 139,820 km (86,880 miles)

Europa

Add the stickers of the Great Red Spot and some of Jupiter's biggest moons. ········>

Callisto

4 FUN JUPITER MOON FACTS

✷ Galileo Galilei discovered Jupiter's four largest moons in the year 1610!

✷ Because Jupiter is such a large planet it has more gravity. Its many moons stay in orbit because gravity pulls them towards Jupiter.

✷ Jupiter's moon Ganymede is the largest moon in the Solar System.

✷ Io, another of Jupiter's moons, has over 400 active volcanoes, making it the most volcanically active object in the Solar System.

Great Red Spot

Io

Ganymede

SATURN

Welcome to Saturn, the second biggest planet in our Solar System. Just don't try to step on its surface – Saturn is made almost entirely of gas. But it's so light, if you could place it on water it would float!

PLANET PROFILE

Distance from Sun:
1.4 billion km
(870 million miles)

Average Temperature:
–140°C (–220°F)

Moons: Around 61, with more discovered almost every year!

Diameter: 120,000 km (74,565 miles) – 764 Earths would fit in Saturn.

Colour Saturn in yellow, brown and orange.

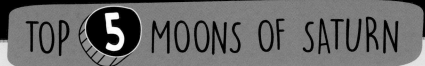

TOP (5) MOONS OF SATURN

Add the stickers of these famous moons.

Titan is slightly larger than the planet Mercury.

Iapetus is two-tone – half the planet appears almost black and the other half almost white.

Find the glow-in-the-dark sticker of the Saturn space probe Cassini-Huygens.

Saturn's rings are made of millions of pieces of ice and rock.

③ SATURN RING FACTS

❋ The distance across Saturn's outermost ring is up to 300,000 km (186,411 miles).

❋ Saturn's main rings can be as little as 10 m (33 ft) thick.

❋ If Saturn was the size of a basketball, the rings would be less than $\frac{1}{250}$th the thickness of a human hair!

 Mimas has a giant crater covering almost a third of its face.

Enceladus has an ocean under its icy surface, where life might exist.

 Phoebe is one of the most ancient objects in our Solar System. It is thought to be almost 4.5 billion years old.

URANUS AND NEPTUNE

Uranus and Neptune are known as the 'ice giants' as they both have rock and ice at their cores.

③ FUN ICE–GIANT FACTS

✦ Uranus is different from other planets as it spins on its side. Nights and days can last about 40 years at each of its poles.

✦ Neptune has the strongest winds in the Solar System reaching speeds up to 2,000 km/h (1,250 mi/h).

✦ Like Jupiter and Saturn, Uranus and Neptune are also called 'gas giants' as they are mostly gas, despite having rock and ice at their core.

URANUS

PLANET PROFILE

Distance from Sun:
2.9 billion km
(1.8 billion miles)

Average Temperature:
−216°C (−357°F)

Moons: 27

Diameter: 50,700 km
(31,504 miles)

PLANET PROFILE

Distance from Sun:
4.5 billion km
(2.8 billion miles)

Average Temperature:
−214°C (−353°F)

Moons: 13

Diameter: 49,200 km
(30,571 miles)

NEPTUNE

4 GAS GIANTS

Use the corresponding stickers to fill in the gaps of these gas-giant sequences.

ASTEROID AND KUIPER BELTS

Beyond Mars, a huge ring of rocks marks the edge of the Inner Solar System. This is called the Asteroid Belt because it contains billions of lumps of metal or rock that are known as asteroids.

The Kuiper Belt stretches from the edge of Neptune's orbit to at least 7.5 billion km (4.7 billion miles) from the Sun.

3 ASTEROID BELT FACTS

- The Asteroid Belt lies roughly between the orbits of Mars and Jupiter.

- Asteroids in the belt vary from tiny dust particles through to the dwarf planet Ceres.

- Gravitational forces can throw asteroids out of the belt towards the Inner Solar System.

Comets are huge lumps of ice that warm up, releasing gases when they pass close to the Sun.

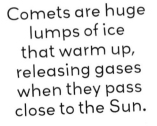

Find the glow-in-the-dark stickers of the comet, Pluto and the rocket.

Pluto is a 'dwarf' planet living within the Kuiper Belt. For a long time it was considered to be the ninth planet of the Solar System. The difference between them is that a dwarf planet has not cleared the area around its orbit of other planets and significant space matter through its gravitational force, while a planet has.

Navigate your spaceship through the Kuiper Belt to reach Pluto.

③ KUIPER BELT FACTS

✳ Scientists believe that left-over objects from the Sun and the planets when they were formed were pushed towards the edge of the Solar System by larger planets, like Jupiter and Saturn, which formed the Kuiper belt.

✳ The Kuiper Belt is much larger than the Asteroid Belt, as much as 20 times the width.

✳ The objects in the Kuiper Belt are made of frozen liquids, gases, rocks and metals.

THE MILKY WAY AND BEYOND

Our Solar System is part of a galaxy called the Milky Way. Look up at the night sky and you'll often see the Milky Way looking like a wispy cloud. It's actually a collection of millions of stars of different sizes, colours and temperatures. It takes around 230 million years for our Solar System to travel once around the centre of the Milky Way.

3 STAR FACTS

- ❂ Most stars are about the size of the Sun. They look tiny in the sky because they are so far away.

- ❂ When stars heat up they begin to shine.

- ❂ Stars are huge balls of glowing gas and dust. The hottest are seen as blue, the second hottest are yellow and the coolest are red.

4 SPACE FEATURES

Can you see these things in the Milky Way?

Cosmic Dust consists of tiny particles of solid material that float between the stars and the planets. It has even been found on Earth.

Red Giants are dying stars that have used up all their fuel. As a result, they expand hugely forming a giant red balloon shape as helium builds up inside. In about five billion years, the Sun will be a red giant.

Find the glow-in-the-dark stickers of these galaxy types.

Spiral

Barred Spiral

Irregular

Lenticular

A **supernova** is a huge explosion caused when a really big star runs out of fuel to burn. Supergiants are the biggest stars and live for the shortest time.

A **black hole** can be found at the heart of most large galaxies. Black holes can contain as much material as 2.5 million stars.

PLANET PUZZLES

Now that you've toured around the Solar System, and beyond, let's see what you've learned!
Tick the boxes to answer TRUE or FALSE to the quiz questions.
Find the matching planet stickers to complete the page.

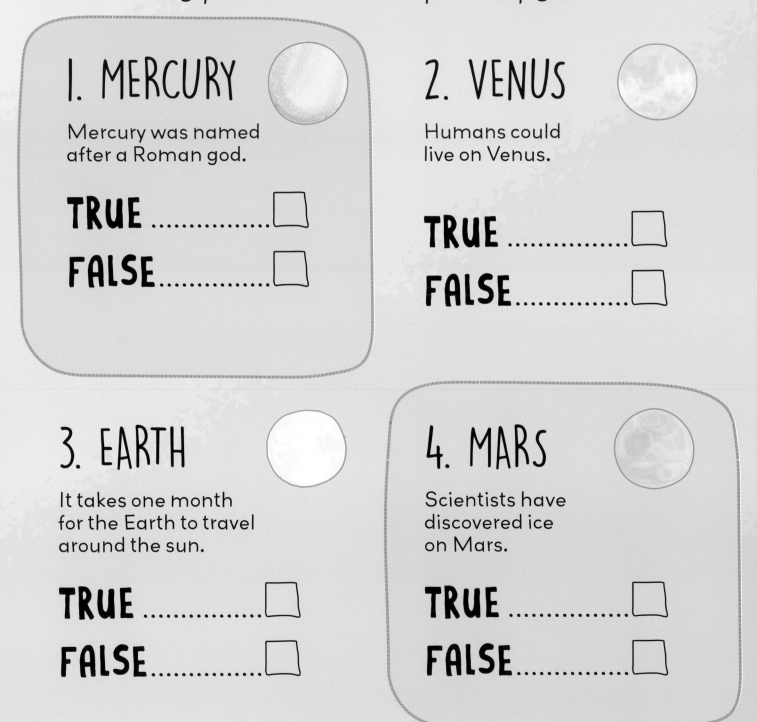

1. MERCURY

Mercury was named after a Roman god.

TRUE .... ☐
FALSE .... ☐

2. VENUS

Humans could live on Venus.

TRUE .... ☐
FALSE .... ☐

3. EARTH

It takes one month for the Earth to travel around the sun.

TRUE .... ☐
FALSE .... ☐

4. MARS

Scientists have discovered ice on Mars.

TRUE .... ☐
FALSE .... ☐

5. JUPITER

Jupiter is the smallest planet in our Solar System.

TRUE .... ☐

FALSE .... ☐

6. SATURN

Saturn's main rings can be as little as 1 cm (0.4 in) thick.

TRUE .... ☐

FALSE .... ☐

7. URANUS

Uranus spins on its side.

TRUE .... ☐

FALSE .... ☐

8. NEPTUNE

Neptune has ice at its core.

TRUE .... ☐

FALSE .... ☐

Now check the answers and see how you did!

I got 7–8 questions right.

Wow! Are you already a space scientist at NASA or the European Space Agency?

I got 4–6 questions right.

You're not quite a qualified space scientist yet, but you're nearly there!

I got 0–3 questions right.

Looks like you're still at the start of your space-scientist career. Keep working at it!

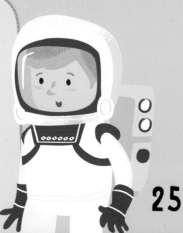

THE SPACE RACE

The Space Race was a race between countries (particularly Russia and the USA) to lead the world in space exploration. This began in 1957 when the Russians launched Sputnik 1. After this, the Americans and Russians competed to develop better and better technology. In 1969, American astronauts successfully landed on the Moon.

Complete the timeline by adding glow-in-the-dark stickers.

1958
America joins the space race by launching the Explorer 1 satellite.

1957
Laika, a Russian dog, is the first living thing to fly in space. She is followed by the first human-made satellite.

1959
Russia's Luna 2 becomes the first spacecraft to reach the Moon.

1961
Russian astronaut Yuri Gagarin is the first human to fly in space on Vostok 1.

1961
Alan B. Shepard is the first American to make a space flight.

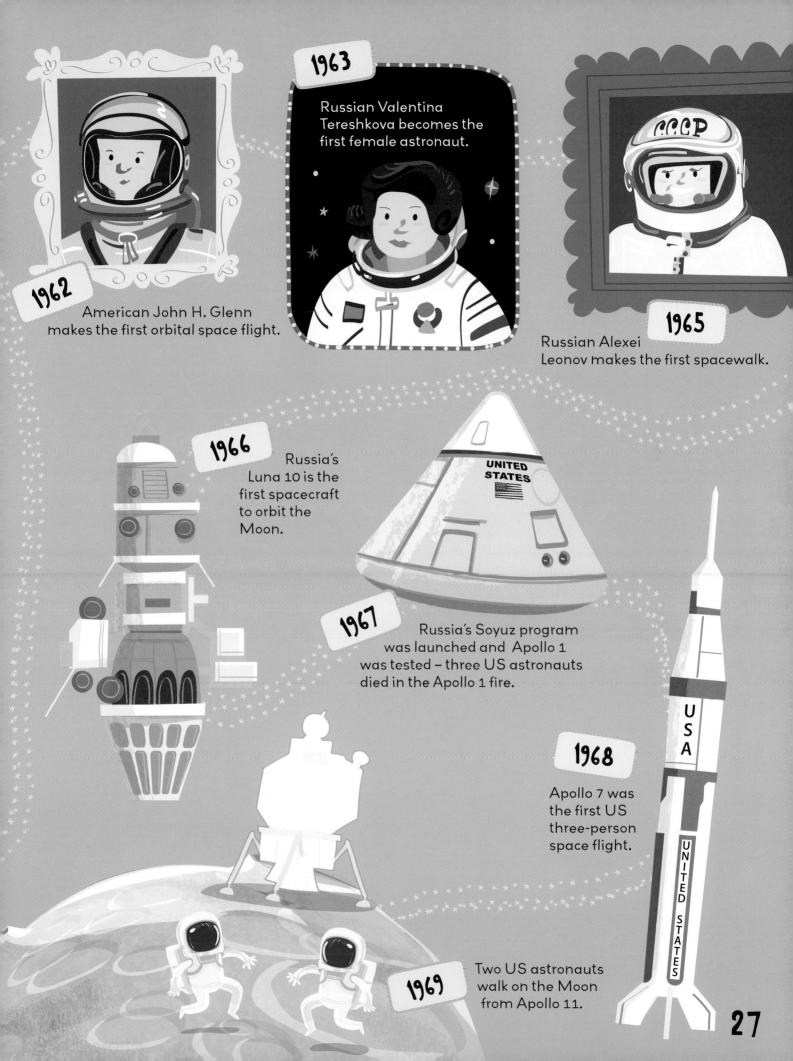

1962 American John H. Glenn makes the first orbital space flight.

1963 Russian Valentina Tereshkova becomes the first female astronaut.

1965 Russian Alexei Leonov makes the first spacewalk.

1966 Russia's Luna 10 is the first spacecraft to orbit the Moon.

UNITED STATES

1967 Russia's Soyuz program was launched and Apollo 1 was tested – three US astronauts died in the Apollo 1 fire.

1968 Apollo 7 was the first US three-person space flight.

USA

UNITED STATES

1969 Two US astronauts walk on the Moon from Apollo 11.

27

SECRETS OF THE SKY

The very best views of our Solar System and beyond come from the amazing Hubble Space Telescope. In 1990, the Hubble was the first telescope to be placed in space. Far above the atmosphere, the Hubble has an uninterrupted view of the Universe so scientists can observe the most distant stars and galaxies.

GALILEO GALILEI

Colour in Galileo as he watches the night sky.

In the 17th century, Galileo Galilei built a telescope and discovered four of Jupiter's moons. He also made a map of the mountains on the Moon.

Add the stickers to the Hubble Telescope.

The Hubble telescope was named after Edwin Hubble, who, in 1923, discovered that our galaxy is just one of many in the Universe.

29

EARLY SPACE TRIPS

Russia first took the lead in the Space Race with Sputnik 1 and 2 in 1957, and a dog called Laika proved that living things could survive in space. The first human to fly in space was Russian astronaut Yuri Gagarin, travelling in Vostok 1.

SPACECRAFT PROFILE

Name: Sputnik 2

Launched: 3rd Nov 1957

Launched by: USSR

Size: 508 kg (1,120 pounds)

Mission Type: To prove living things could survive in space

Destination: Earth orbit

Find the glow-in-the-dark sticker of Laika the dog.

Russia's Luna 2 was the first spacecraft to reach the Moon in 1959. It took 35 hours.

2 SPACE TRAVEL FACTS

✷ In 1959 Russia's Luna 1 was the first spacecraft to leave Earth's orbit.

✷ The first US astronaut to make a space flight was Alan B. Shepard in 1961. The flight lasted 15 minutes 22 seconds.

SPACECRAFT PROFILE

Name: Vostok 1

Launched: 12th April 1961

Launched by: USSR

Weight: 4,725 kg (10,417 pounds)

Mission Type: To test the effects of space flight on the human body

Destination: Earth orbit

Find the glow-in-the-dark sticker of Yuri Gagarin.

MOON LANDINGS

We know more about the Moon than any other place in the Solar System (apart from Earth) because it is the only place that humans have visited. Russia first sent a probe, Luna 2, in 1959 and ten years later Apollo 11 landed on the Moon. Astronauts Neil Armstrong and Buzz Aldrin bounced around the rocky surface. Today lunar probes rather than humans are sent to gather information about the Moon.

Add the glow-in-the-dark stickers of Earth and the astronaut, and then find six differences between the two pictures.

SPACECRAFT PROFILE

Name: Apollo 11

Launched: 16th July 1969

Launched by: NASA Kennedy Space Centre

Weight: 28,801 kg (63,495 pounds)

Mission Type: Manned lunar landing

Destination: The Moon

3 MOON DISCOVERIES

✴ Footprints left by the astronauts on the Moon could last forever as there is no air to blow the dust away!

✴ Large craters on the Moon measuring 160 km (100 miles) across were caused by asteroids crashing there.

✴ In 1972, Apollo 17 landing module Challenger discovered areas of orange soil on the Moon resulting from ancient volcanic eruptions.

LIFT-OFF!

A huge team of scientists, engineers and mathematicians will have worked for years to prepare a space rocket for lift-off. When launch day arrives, it's not just the astronauts who hold their breath!

Complete the timeline by adding the glow-in-the-dark rocket stickers.

SPACECRAFT PROFILE

Name: Space Shuttle Columbia

Launched: 12th April 1981

Launched by : NASA Kennedy Space Centre

Weight: 2,041 tonnes (2,250 US tons)

Mission Type: Multiple

Destination: Earth orbit

⑤ STAGES OF LAUNCH

1. 5, 4, 3, 2, 1 – the solid rocket boosters and main engine fire up and you have LIFT-OFF!

2. The shuttle clears the launch tower.

3. In less than three minutes the two solid rocket boosters burn out and separate before parachuting back to Earth.

2 SHUTTLE FACTS

✸ In January 1986, Space Shuttle Challenger exploded over Cape Canaveral, Florida, USA, just seconds after lift-off. All seven crew were killed.

✸ The second space shuttle disaster occurred in 2003 when Columbia disintegrated on re-entering Earth's atmosphere, killing the crew of seven.

4. The fuel tank drops off when the fuel is used up. The main engine uses less power as the rocket flies higher.

5. Eight minutes after take-off the shuttle approaches Earth orbit. From here the astronauts can see the curve of Earth.

INTERNATIONAL SPACE STATION

The International Space Station (ISS) is a gigantic laboratory in space. Here astronauts and scientists from all over the world live for up to a year carrying out all kinds of experiments, such as the effects of space on humans and animals.

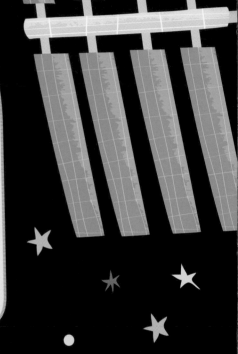

3 FUN ISS FACTS

- ✸ The huge solar panels of the Space Station catch the Sun's rays and change them into electricity to keep the station running.

- ✸ The Space Station is growing all the time as new modules are brought by different missions.

- ✸ Scientists float in the station but if they need to sit down they hook their feet under special loops on the floor.

INSIDE ISS

OUTSIDE ISS

Add stickers to finish the Space-Station picture.

SPACE HALL OF FAME

All of these people have made a huge contribution to space exploration.
Add the stickers to complete the hall of fame.

Yuri Gagarin was the first human in space. In 1961 he orbited Earth in Vostok 1.

Alan B. Shepard travelled in Mercury 3 in 1961. He proved that a person could control a spacecraft while weightless.

John H Glenn circled Earth three times in under five hours in Mercury 6 in 1962.

Valentina Tereshkova was a parachutist before becoming the first female astronaut. She orbited Earth in 1963.

Ed White made the first US spacewalk and tested a 'zip gun' designed to help astronauts move in space.

Vladimir Komarov was a pilot on the Voshkod 1, which was the first flight with more than one crew member.

Neil Armstrong was the first human to walk on the Moon.

Buzz Aldrin accompanied Neil Armstrong on Apollo 11 in 1969 and also walked on the Moon.

Draw your hall-of-fame picture here.

What could you do to become a famous astronaut, scientist or engineer? Write your story here.

ASTRONAUT TRAINING

Training for astronauts has changed a lot from the early days of space exploration. Today astronauts train for two years in classrooms, 'dummy' spacecraft and simulators. The use of virtual reality has greatly helped prepare astronauts for space trips.

Trainee astronauts practise spacewalking in giant water tanks. The density of the water helps them to float as if they are weightless.

Find the sticker of the astronaut in training.

Virtual reality simulation helps trainees feel like they are moving around a cabin or working on the Space Station.

SPACE CADET

Draw yourself as an astronaut. Remember to give yourself a special badge.

VOYAGER 1 AND 2

Every day we are learning more about space and the American Voyager is an example of a program that continues to increase our knowledge of the outer Solar System. Voyager 1 and Voyager 2 are two robotic probes originally sent to explore Saturn and Jupiter. Since the launch of the Voyagers in 1977, they have reached beyond the orbits of Neptune and Pluto.

SPACECRAFT PROFILE

Name: Voyager 1

Launched: 5th Sept 1977

Launched by : NASA Kennedy Space Centre (Cape Canaveral)

Weight: 825 kg (1,820 pounds)

Mission Type: 'Fly-by' exploration of outer planets

Destination: Jupiter, Saturn and its moon Titan, interstellar space

The 1 and 2 Voyagers were the first human-made objects to enter interstellar space, which is the space that exists between star systems in the galaxy.

Navigate Voyager 2 through interstellar space to the centre of the star maze.

....: Add a glow-in-the-dark sticker of Voyager 2.

3 VOYAGER 1 AND 2 FACTS

❋ Voyager 1 and 2 are the oldest active probes in deep space.

❋ Voyager 1 took about 32,000 pictures of Jupiter, Saturn and their moons and rings.

❋ Today Voyager 1 is over 20 billion km (13 billion miles) away.

SPACE ROVERS

Scientists are constantly developing vehicles for roaming around space. The Lunar Roving Vehicle is an electric car that helped astronauts explore the moon. But the Moon is not the only planet where we have rover vehicles.

ROVER PROFILE

Name: Mars Rover Curiosity

Launched: 26th November 2011

Launched by : NASA Kennedy Space Centre

Weight: 900 kg (2,000 pounds)

Mission Type: Mars exploration

Destination: Mars

SPACE ROVER

Draw and decorate your own space rover.

2 FACTS ABOUT OTHER MARS ROVERS

✹ NASA's Mars Exploration Rover mission is an ongoing robotic space mission launched in 2003 with two rovers called **Spirit** and **Opportunity**.

✹ The rovers have collected dust and rocks from Mars and taken pictures, which has given scientists important information about Mars.

Find the glow-in-the-dark sticker of this rover on Mars.

NEW PLANET DISCOVERED!

Imagine that you have made astronomy history by discovering a completely new planet! Share your findings with the world by filling in the report and profile. Decide what type of planet this is — gas, ice or something completely different!

SPACE TIMES

Fill in the blanks and draw your very own planet.

The space scientist _____ discovered
[YOUR NAME]

a new planet. They called it_____.
[YOUR PLANET'S NAME]

YOUR PLANET PROFILE

Distance from Sun:

Average Temperature:

Moons:

Size:

Fill in the planet profile for your new discovery.

Use the stickers to make an alien for your planet.

Describe to the world how to reach this planet and why people should visit.

47

TRAINEE ASTRONAUT

So you want to be an astronaut. First you have to pass this quiz! Read through the previous pages to find the answers.

1. FIRST ASTRONAUT

Who was the first human to travel in space?

....

....

2. SATELLITE

The Americans were the first to send a satellite into space.

TRUE .... ☐

FALSE .... ☐

3. ZERO GRAVITY

How does an astronaut practise weightlessness?

....

....

4. SPACE PROBES

What are the oldest active probes in space?

....

....

5. LABORATORY

What is the name of the giant laboratory in space?

....

....

When you've answered all the questions reward yourself with these stickers.

Answers: 1. Yuri Gagarin; 2. FALSE; 3. By practising in a huge water tank; 4. Voyager 1 and 2; 5. The International Space Station